THE BIG GREEN

POETRY MACHINE

An Ocean Of Words

Edited By Daisy Job

First published in Great Britain in 2023 by:

Young Writers
Remus House
Coltsfoot Drive
Peterborough
PE2 9BF
Telephone: 01733 890066
Website: www.youngwriters.co.uk

Printed and bound in the UK by BookPrintingUK
Website: www.bookprintinguk.com
YB0542CZ

FOREWORD

Welcome Reader,

For Young Writers' latest competition The Big Green Poetry Machine, we asked primary school pupils to craft a poem about the world. From nature and environmental issues to exploring their own habitats or those of others around the globe, it provided pupils with the opportunity to share their thoughts and feelings about the world around them.

Here at Young Writers our aim is to encourage creativity in children and to inspire a love of the written word, so it's great to get such an amazing response, with some absolutely fantastic poems. It's important for children to be aware of the world around them and some of the issues we face, but also to celebrate what makes it great! This competition allowed them to express their hopes and fears or simply write about their favourite things. The Big Green Poetry Machine gave them the power of words and the result is a wonderful collection of inspirational and moving poems in a variety of poetic styles.

I'd like to congratulate all the young poets in this anthology; I hope this inspires them to continue with their creative writing.

NATURE   WILDLIFE   INSECTS   EARTH   RECYCLE

CONTENTS

Independent Entries

Shaina France-Scotland (9)	110	Hope Whittaker (11)	154
Kaleia Peres (7)	111	Sophia Tuffaha (5)	155
Lacey Cameron (10)	112	Muhammed Khizar Khan (8)	156
Yuvraj Minhas (6)	113	Sue'ad Nazrana (9)	157
Nusayba Ahmed (11)	114	Habib Parvez (7)	158
Logan Fullerton (7)	115	Violet Hall (8)	159
Lilly Newman (10)	116	Sophia Nanouri (9)	160
Taylor Hotchkiss (11)	117	Evie Kairo (5)	161
Ayla Tuffaha (6)	118	Eleanor-Marie Hammerton (9)	162
Jimmy Smith (8)	119	Louisa Gribben (10)	163
Rosie Barnes (10)	120	Elowyn Blackburn (6)	164
Ava Hutton (9)	121	Jasmine Jenkins (9)	165
Safiya Khan (11)	122	Zeke Tunbridge (9)	166
Daisy Duffield (8)	123	Hajra Latif (9)	167
Phoebe Mace (8)	124	Oscar Butler-Addis (10)	168
Shreya Sapkota (7)	125	Hibba Noor (11)	169
Lucia Palmer (9)	126	Jack Dove (8)	170
Oliver Morgan (8)	127	Zara Firmin (9)	171
Bobby Fisher (9)	128	Harry Alessandar (12)	172
Maryam Ibrahim (6)	129	William Thomas (10)	173
Adam Umar (7)	130	Rosie Dobson (6)	174
Zoe Tsitouridis (8)	131	Bakhtawar Yousaf (6)	175
Madeleine Heap (9)	132	Joshua Tanimowo (6)	176
Michelle Akadiri	133	Isla Marshall (10)	177
Isabella Nikolov (9)	134	Zuriel Oyedeji (7)	178
Carrie Wang (11)	135	Munachi Ojediran (8)	179
Scarlett Impey (10)	136	Zara Kelf (9)	180
Alice Formoy (13)	137	Mahalakshmi Duraiarasan (11)	181
Muna White (11)	138	Chrysanthea Davies Nkansa (7)	182
Thailula Thompson (10)	140	Isabella Henderson (8)	183
George Frank Gamble (9)	141	May Luna Estwick (6)	184
Tvisha Suchak (10)	142	Ettie Jones (6)	185
Edward McFarland (7)	143	Divyansh Singh (10)	186
Kushy Kaur (10)	144	Kat McCue (7)	187
Ameena Adil (7)	145	Ajan Kola (7)	188
Archie Mould (11)	146	Beatrice Peacock (10)	189
Mason Sejpal (9)	147	Sophia Mazouzi (6)	190
Luqman Ahmad (9)	148	Brook Laycock (10)	191
Thomas McDonnell (11)	149	Ruby Fairweather (8)	192
Betsy Young (8)	150	Henry Bryers (10)	193
Milena Blackburn (9)	151	Alexander Bak (7)	194
Amelia Reilly (10)	152	Isen Miller (9)	195
Millie Purcell (9)	153	Emily Oppersdorff (8)	196

Frank Morris (10)	197
Ava Rees (9)	198
Sotirios Nanouris (5)	199
Yuveer Goenka (9)	200
Willow Gage (6)	201
Emilia Menezes-Shotter (7)	202
Isla Walker (11)	203
Alexandru Gabriel Paclisan (9)	204
Layla Sullivan (6)	205
Lorelai Earl (11)	206
Alice Fletcher (5)	207
Phoebe Charlesworth (7)	208
Logan Watkin (9)	209
Priscilla Suresh (8)	210
Macy Ludgate (9)	211
Sophia Tang (8)	212
Kimberley Nindi (9)	213
Arthur Woods-Carrick (7)	214
Isla Reeves (7)	215
Jake Brzezinski (5)	216
Sion Guan (6)	217
Sujay Thiruvallar (7)	218
Beatrice Isaac (9)	219
Sky Tsz Kwok (8)	220

THE POEMS

Don't Litter

P lastic is not fantastic,
R efuse, reuse, repair, repurpose, rehome,
O ur rubbish all goes out to sea,
T he sea creatures need us more than ever,
E ven though we pollute we could still help,
C limate change can be very difficult,
T he Earth can count on us.

T hey all are going to be endangered,
H ow are we going to help the planet?
E arth has over 200 million pieces of rubbish every day.

P lant a tree to help our environment,
L et animals be free and plastic free,
A nd food, don't buy a product that has palm oil in,
N ever ever buy a forest and cut it down,
E nd the suffering animals,
T he right thing to do is to put rubbish in the bins.

Savanna Smith (9)

The Marvellous World

A privileged civilisation humans are, to have the
glorious Earth
With its distinctive life forms and natural
spectacles
They are a phosphorescent veil from the reality,
that few see, but only from a different angle
Man sees the innocent red pandas vivaciously
pirouette, leap and bound
But a scarce number of men are aware of what
their species number comes around
All animals fight with their soul, mind and every
fibre of their being, just to procure food from the
leftover trees,
While the majority of mankind idly relax, never
having experienced dearth.

An example of what man already has are the
pulchritudinous Northern Lights.
Like silvery strings slithering here and there on a
harp in heaven, they elegantly flit around, as
though dancing.
Like a perfect piece of art, produced by the
painstaking brushstrokes of a dextrous hand, its
scintillating light radiates as though prancing.

The delicious florescence of the viridescent,
entwining in a helix with the iridescent hue of pink,
demonstrates a purity unbeknownst to man.
It swathes you with exhilaration and perplexity; its
grace flooding a mind's span
In the ethereal sky, it nestles, levitated in the
heights.

Humans are gradually diminishing the
splendiferous beauty of our planet
With every step in the wrong direction, mankind's
actions become ever more irreversible
Soon people shall lament and mourn their
obliviously cruel actions when the damage will
clearly be visible
What exists now is truly wondrous, and preserving
it is a necessity
After all, this rotund sphere, containing all of these
wonders, is man's true destiny
Attentiveness and care for this place should now
be a habit.

Arnav Ghoshal (11)

Fighting For Our Rivers And Oceans

Our rivers and oceans are precious,
beautiful and fun,
Full of plant-life and creatures
living in harmony.
Children playing at the water's edge,
unaware of the
dangers
below.

Plastic bottles, bags and straws
choking
the life out of turtles, seals and whales.
Penguins, sharks and seagulls
sick and injured, by
careless
pollution and
waste.

Big, greedy companies
belching their

poison
into the water,
protected by
lying politicians
who pretend it's not there.

What can we do?
How can we help?

We can change!

We can fight!

More recycling.
Less litter.
Clean our *gasping* waterways.
Allow them to
Breathe
once again.
Educate
the world to
do better.

And FIGHT!
Fight the lazy governments.

Fight the dirty businesses.
Protests and petitions,
activism and banners.
Make our voices heard!

Changes can be made.

We *can* save our rivers and oceans.

We *can* help our animals.

We *can* protect the planet
for children to keep playing,
in safety,
at the water's edge.

We *can* save everyone and everything
if we work together,
with *hope* for a
better,
cleaner
future.

Amelie Bell (10)

Save The Animals

All animals are special,
All animals are unique,
All animals have special qualities,
Koalas hold on their trees
Same with orangutans and sloths
Who hang on them like a loose branch,
And pandas which live within the depths of the
huge, friendly forest.
The woodcutter men come and chop down their
homes
Chip chop chip chop
Bushfires start from climate changes,
Burning and killing innocent animals' homes,
How will we know if we'll have panda bears or
orangutans and sloths that hang on trees or cute,
grey koalas that hold on their property.
We won't know if we'll have all of that in a few
years' time,
If the worst tends to happen we won't have a
huge, friendly forest or cute, cuddly animals
Our world won't be the same.

Victoria Maleki (10)

The Sea And Me

I am lucky, you see,
My house overlooks the deep blue sea.
One morning, when I felt alone,
Why he couldn't stay was *not known*.

The very next day, I ran down to the bay.
He was *calm*, so I could stay.
After a while, we played our game: I would fling, he would bring.
Then he said, "I cannot stay, I cannot play anymore today."
So, he went away.

The very next day, I ran down to the beach.
He was *angry*, he was out of reach.
After a while, he calmed down, we played our game, I did not fear to drown.
Then he said, "I cannot stay, I cannot play anymore today."
So, he went away.

The very next day, I ran down to the sands.
He was *sad*, he did not hold on to my hands.

After a while, he was not so upset, we played our
game, we watched the sunset.
Then he said, "I cannot stay, I cannot play anymore
today."
So, he went away.

The very next day, I ran down to the shore.
He was *happy*, I was one hundred percent sure.
After a while, we both could see: It is to be, the sea
and me.
Then he said, "I cannot stay, I cannot play anymore
today."
So, he went away.

I am lucky, you see,
I am friends with the deep blue sea.
I now understand; the sea you can never own.
Why he couldn't stay is *now known*.

Felipe George Lemos Thompson

The Planet Matters

The planet needs our help, it's getting damaged
fast!
It shouldn't be on your list for saving last
The weather patterns are changing, it's a disaster!
The weather gets weirder even faster and faster.

It's global warming,
The people's last warning
The icebergs are floating out to sea
It's just as if mankind just want to disagree.

Stop cutting trees, for goodness' sake!
They're alive, they're not fake!
Does mankind want nature to really be there?
Because we are throwing nature into depths of
despair.

It wasn't like this before
Mankind is damaging it more and more
You're not the only one out there campaigning for
the planet's rights
You're not the only one out there protecting the
planet's beautiful sights

So make your voice count, let them know it's you!
Make them see from your side of view!

Let them hear your voice!
Let them hear your special choice!
You're the shining star in the crowd
Let them hear your voice nice and loud

It's global warming,
The people's last warning,
We need to help the universe because it's getting worse,
Because mankind has diagnosed it with a deadly curse.

Help the planet, it's getting piled with lots of rubbish
And in the sea it affects, for example, the fish
For the planet to be clean is not a wish

And now I'll tell you this problem has not just begun
We need to finish it now so it'll finally be done.

The planet matters.

Mehreen Azim (10)

Our World

Our world is full of beauty and lots of fantastic sights,
Natural wonders, buildings and trees of every height,

Bees and birds and insects,
Wildlife big and small,
So hard to choose a favourite, I really love them all,

The tiny mice that scurry here and there, always in a hurry,
To elephants who stomp about the land,
So big and large and beautiful, they really are so grand,
To trees and lakes and rivers, mountains and sandy beaches,
Each and every one of them has learning that it teaches,

When I look around me,
I realise what's going on,
I see clouds and skies and sunshine,
And know what's going wrong,

Our Mother Earth is crying and our Mother Earth is
sad she's given us this beauty,
And we are turning it all bad,

We need to take a moment,
We need to stop and think,
If we don't change the way we are,
The world will be over in a blink,

All of us people, babies to children and the elders
too,
Need to stop and take a minute, here's what we
can do,

Recycle more, only buy what you need,
Keep rubbish out of the seas,
Take care of our surroundings, help to plant new
trees,
And if you feel you can do more don't forget our
bees,

If we all help out and try to do all these,
Mother Earth will be so pleased,

And I can guarantee and I'm sure that each and every person will agree,
It will really make the Earth a much better place to be.

Madison King (7)

An Important Blessing

We can save and change the world together
Like a group of clouds changing the weather
Nature is amazing, it sounds so wonderful
It's an astonishing blessing which is so cool
Try it one morning and listen to the symphony of
nature
The morning birds and all types of creature
There is a message I would like to say
Humans kill the animals in forests and ruin their
environment
They are like raiders and are so arrogant
If this destruction keeps on happening, Earth won't
have a life
Let's all help to save and protect our planet
without any strife
Here are some tips to make a change
Reuse, reduce, recycle
Save oil and diesel and petrol, so instead go to
places by cycle
Use 100% renewable energy
Make a change and let it forever be!

Ameenah Hameed (10)

Understanding Our Situation

There's only one Earth,
There's no Planet B,
It's not like it can just rebirth.
But that's not the worst,
Haven't you heard?
There are powerful countries that cause pollution,
However,
The countries that are causing 1% of pollution are
suffering the most.
Animals are becoming extinct quicker,
Like how there are only 60 Jarvan rhinos left,
Hurry, the pollution is getting thicker!
How about recycling?
That's more eco-friendly,
What about cycling instead of cars that produce
fumes?
42 million trees are getting cut every day!
We could stop cutting down trees,
Well maybe we could ask tree cutters to do it less.
In summer trees bring a nice breeze,

But they also give us the oxygen we breathe.
Earth is a great place to be,
But if we are not eco-friendly,
Then it won't.
So let's work together,
And bring Planet Earth,
To its former glory.
Let's start a plan...

Reduce, reuse, recycle,
Ask to buy tree seeds and grow a tree or two,
Walk or cycle to places if possible.
If we all do this we could stop climate change!
We just have to work together!

Aminah Badjan (10)

I Am... Planet Earth

I am precious and indispensible
I wonder if there are others like me
I hear the sound of my wonderful, essential trees
screaming in pain whilst being violently chopped
down
I see the image of my disastrous future lying
before me
I want to tell all of the humans on me to stop
harming my beautiful self
I am precious and indispensible

I pretend to be healthy and in shape to my
neighbours
(But I know I'm not)
I feel the anger burning up inside me thanks to
climate change
I touch my warm waters and decreasing forests
I worry that soon climate change will take over
I cry when I see myself getting polluted and my
beloved nature disappearing
I am precious and indispensible

I understand that some humans are being cruel to me;
Others are just trying to help me
I say to myself every second that everything will be alright
I dream myself as glorious as can be - with endless sources of water, woodland and inhabitants
I try to comfort myself and stray away from worry and anger
I hope that soon I'll be back to normal again
I am... Planet Earth.

Bianca Lofino Aquilina (11)

Tomorrow

I wonder what tomorrow will bring
Will it be woeful enough to cry
Or even happy and cheery so that I'll sing?
I want to ask tomorrow of why
Why do you hate patiently waiting?
Why can't you stop and live in each moment
When you can sleep and sleep in so then
You don't have to wake up feeling old and drained
And stay in the moment of yesterday?

Oh tomorrow, why do you have to chase me?
No matter how fast I run I never have enough time
Let me be peaceful and you might see
That you don't always have to take what's mine.

Why can't I stay in today? In this hour. This minute.
Second.
Why does time have to move forward?
Why can't it stay still?
You don't have to beat a record.

It seems as though every time you come
You catch me quicker than the time before

We aren't fighting, and this isn't a war
If it is I give up, tomorrow. You've won.

You mix up my words so that
I will not make any sense
Give me a date, don't leave me in suspense.

Why do I have to follow what you say
When I can be happy in yesterday?

Elizabeth Grace (10)

Four Seasons

Winter comes and devours the plants of our land
No green is left, just rocks and sand
As cold grips our world, flowers wither and die
But it must be so, and so we go on by

Spring brings new hope as things start to grow
Leaves on their tree, flowers on their meadow
New life is born as chicks start to peep
And hedgehogs and bears awake from their sleep

Summer, the most bright and happy season of the
year
Warm holidays as you draw loved ones near
Windows are open in hope of a breeze
As fruit and berries blossom on trees

Autumn arrives and leaves turn to red
Falling off trees and onto the ground instead
The nights grow longer and the days more cold
It has gone in a circle since the days of old

It comes back to winter as leaves fall all around
And squirrels bury their nuts underground

Rooting through grass are badgers and hares
Whilst hibernation begins for hedgehogs and bears

The year comes around and too soon ends
But another year is coming with family and friends
You can have fun and play with them with glee
And now, I wish you a happy 2023!

Millie Rosel (11)

The Green Rhyme Tree

To make our world more green
All kids should join in!
To draw a tree of ideas
I have so many, they hurt my daddy's ears!

If we all join together
Our Earth will last forever
I spent a day rhyming
To ensure our tree is thriving

Each branch will carry a guide
To more ideas on the side
The ideas will light it
To win this war, let's fight it!

First branch
Is about my lunch
Pack green
What do you mean?

Water bottle
Has a motto

Less plastic
Is fantastic!

A sponsored bottle
Made of metal
Will be so cool
And environmental

I have a hunch
To pack my lunch
With less red meat
For me to eat

The second branch
Says my clothes
Dress to impress
But buy less

Reuse your clothes
The shop's not closed
Your eco shoes
Can then grow shoots!

The third branch
Travels fast!

Make haste
But zero waste!

To go to school
Don't be a fool
Walk, cycle or run
Electric car is also fun!

Once inside continue the fight
We need the light but make it right
Solar panels, LED lamps
Draft proof windows and grow our own plants!

Nicholas Christodoulou (6)

Save Our Planet

I don't want to protect the environment,
I want to create a world where the environment
doesn't need protecting any more.
We need to protect our wonderful nature to give
us hope for a better future.
So please don't give up now, there is still much
more plastic to be picked up.
Just please always remember there is no Planet B!
Every day, eight million pieces of plastic pollution
make their way into our seas!
And we need to protect our blue, sparkling sea.
We need to protect our habitats, to save our
bumblebees.
I wish we knew much sooner and those beautiful
creatures would not be gone any longer.
So let's keep this planet clean that we all adore
and keep it safe forevermore...

Ava Grocutt (11)

The World

Oh world... oh world,
For you were once so beautiful,
For you were once a paradise.

Fuel,
Plastic,
Greenhouse gases,
The pathway to the ending point,
Of the world's masses...

For we all talk about what we will be,
When we grow up,
However...
Do we talk about what the world will be,
When it grows up?

Caring for wildlife,
Saving the planet,
Reducing your carbon footprint,
The world's grand, heroic saviour.

Do you get the gist?

For we all talk about what we will be,
When we grow up,
However...
Do we talk about what the world will be,
When it grows up...?

You can buy another electric Ferrari,
Although it won't come for free,
You can't buy another world,
That will never come cheap,
In fact...

It will never come back.

For we all talk about what we will be,
When we grow up,
However...
Do we talk about what the world will be,
When it grows up...?

Oh world... oh world,
For you could be so beautiful,

If we do our part,
You could once again be a paradise.

A paradise that is born from our hearts.

Sanaa Singh (11)

Animals Need Freedom

Animals are stuck behind a never opening cage,
Trapped behind bars far from their natural habitat
and home,
Fearful and all alone.

They are in a rage,
Stuck behind their never-ending cage
Running up and down in dismay,
Wondering if they will see their family today.

Their environment is no longer protected
Because of man's ever-growing destructive greed.

If we need to look after them to save their species
It should be in their own habitat.

So, we could send them home, it's a start don't you
see!
But how would that affect the economy?

Maybe the businessman would be kind
And not think of the money he's leaving behind,
But of the animal and its right to be free.

Arabella Peres (9)

The Foxes

She streaked like a flash - her fur was bronze
Shimmered in the sun
Her eyes glittered
Hatred? There was none
For all they portrayed was a feeling of hope
All they said was, "We are of great decision."
And when I met those eyes,
They showed me the peace
Of all that can be told
Ahead of her lay
A path scattered with leaves.
Garbage stared - they threw cold glances and shot
some glares
At the peaceful fox family: it was no business of
theirs
That this was lying around their home.
Under the trees lay their underground dome
And her cubs lay sleeping
Sleeping all alone.
They had heard rumours: the foxes are being
hunted, they said
Humans hunt them, not birds instead.

One day the humans arrived: they took away the
small cubs' lives
With a bang!
She tried to run away but she was wounded
She screeched for help but no one came
And now their home is broken
We must carry shame
We must realise, we must treasure
We must see: produce every measure possible
And see that our animals
Are protected from harm.

Zahra Parvez (10)

The Fish's Wish

I cruise through the ocean, joining all my friends
We play tag and hide-and-seek and I swim around all the bends
But what I do not notice, I'm incredibly sad to say
A plastic bag from litterbugs let loose from the quay

I try to turn around and swim but it's much too late
I'm stuck in the plastic bag and now I must wait
I'm waiting and waiting for help to come; my throat is starting to hurt
But even so I cry for help, my eyes on full alert

Then suddenly, two strong hands lift me from the bag
I look up to see the piece of litter held aloft like a flag
A kind face looks down at me, urging me to go and play
I thank them with my eyes and swim away from the bay
I'm grateful for the people like the kind one that helped me

There needs to be more like that to set us fish free
So why don't you be one and put your litter in the bin?
I promise that you won't regret it so please, do listen.

Stop ocean pollution = Save marine life.

Tripti Kurian (10)

This Is An Eco Message

Is it too much to ask for a pollution-free world?
The condition of the environment leaves us appalled.

Can we call this progress if life comes to a halt?
We are responsible for pollution, it is our fault.

Oceans are poisoned by spillings of oil,
Pesticides are contaminating Earth's soil.

It's a pity not to see a clear blue sky,
As air pollution is alarmingly high.

Global temperature is rising, glaciers are melting down,
Inaction by us will let cities drown.

It is not that we don't have a solution,
To tackle and control this ongoing pollution.

Reduce plastic use, stop deforestation,
Plant trees for clean air and soil restoration.

Factories should stop draining waste into the sea,
Then marine life will improve naturally.

Composting can make the soil fertile
And we should not let debris pile.

Henry Opechowski (9)

Plastic Pollution

The ocean is *my* home.
I swim in it every day.
But all I can see is people's plastic.
My home is always looking grey!

The ocean is *my* home
But they throw away their old toys
They throw away their bottles
And plastic bags that just destroy!

Only if they knew...!

The ocean is *my* home.
That is where I am happy
But the people cannot see it
When they throw away an old nappy!

The ocean is *my* home
But it doesn't smell very clean!
It smells like stinky food
And dirty laundry!

The ocean is *my* home
And something needs to change

The people of Planet Earth must find a different way
To throw their rubbish... away!

The ocean is *our* home
The people and the fish
Who like to enjoy its beauty
And not to just throw away their old dish!

I hope I see a new change
Because the ocean is blue
Filled with happy fish
But only if they knew...!

Mallory Yorobe (7)

Help Me Save Our Home

I love Earth because it my home,
It's beautiful place where plants have grown.
Our planet used to be amazing beyond imagining.
People are chopping trees
And throwing plastic in the seas,
But I am very sad about what is happening,
But all these things we ignore.
Animals don't have a house anymore,
Factories and cars and trucks make so much smoke,
And have harmful gases that are no joke.
This is called global warming,
When Earth's heat is collecting.
It's making our planet really hot,
So icebergs are melting really fast.
Polar bears and penguins are all alone,
Stuck on ice all on their own.
We can all help in different ways,
Little by little every day.
Reusing and recycling,

Biking or carpooling
Do these things and help me,
So our beautiful planet we can again see!

Anvie Garg (5)

Our Earth

High up in the clouds
But don't forget to get off
And when you come back,
Look down to how beautiful it is.
How two children run across the fields
Like everyone trying to make friends
We live in peace, harmoniously
Enjoying all that is beautiful.

All nature worships us
And stars, sun, even the moon
And the birds all sing to you
In chorus, a song of peace and blessing.

In front of your great nature
We all pray today and
With a call to the world and
We launch one more hope.

Everywhere is only waste
In food only Es,
Substances and materials

That kill oceans and animals.
Slowly nature dies!

Now if you got off
Meditate in everything you have seen.
It's never too late
To learn to protect all together
One world better to build.

Ayinoor Murray (10)

Listen Up

As the breeze makes the trees sway,
All that rubbish blows away,
Right now the world is full of litter,
Everyone, try and make it better.

Go litter picking, it can be fun,
If we work together the change can be done,
Make sure your rubbish goes in the bin,
Otherwise it will be floating.

Unfortunately, lots of our litter is going into our oceans,
So get moving, put the wheels in motion,
Grab a bag, go down to the beach,
Grab a friend, who else can we teach?

When plastic goes in the sea,
There the animals will be,
Into their homes
Goes your waste and plastic,
They will be extinct unless we do something drastic!

Our world is an amazing place,
One last opportunity to embrace,
One more chance, can't you see?
Listen up, everyone, there is no Planet B!

Minnie Macdonald (9)

Our Wonderful World

Hear the almighty winds as they blow
And the timid trickle of water flow
Watch the clouds drift and hear the sky sing
While aiding the birds and carrying their wings
Our wonderful world

See the delicate branches as they dance in the
gentle breeze,
And the sweet, pretty patterns puddles create
when they freeze
See the glorious pieces of art trees shed every year
As the cold of the winter draws near
Our wonderful world

Feel the softness of the earth as if not to hurt our
feet
And all the precious creatures we have yet to meet
They used to help us like the mighty horse or the
selfless ox
Just so we would have a whole year full of crops
Our wonderful world

I hope we can save our Earth,
It's the sanctuary we live on, with the highest tier
of worth
It's a place we must protect and shelter
So stop releasing more greenhouse gasses before
we melt her.

Aimee Brown

The Pollution Poem

Planet Earth is dying,
Mother Nature is crying,
The animals are fleeing,

We chop the trees,
That give us air,
But keep the cars that give out smoke,
So strong it can harm even a gallant gorilla,

We're running out of time,
The Arctic is melting,
Forests are on fire,
Sea levels are rising,

Pollution causes global warming,
Pollution stains our seas,
Pollution infects our air,
Pollution poisons our plants,

Soon is not enough,
But now is right,
So stop thinking,
And start acting,

We can begin by repairing the damage done,
We must plant trees,
We must reduce, reuse, recycle,
We cause too much pollution,
So let's think of a solution,

It's time to act now
Or there'll be nothing left
For we'll be gone and our beautiful world too,
Save our planet.

Kohinoorjot Kaur (9)

Elephants - Count Them While You Can

1,000 miles away,
A young elephant and his herd are travelling day
by day.
Enormous and mighty but an endangered species,
By men and his guns, are brought to their knees.

Their ivory tusks are of great value,
And so, we must protect them! Can you?
As their feet stomp across the earth,
Somewhere, an elephant mum gives birth.

They are in trouble and great danger,
Getting shot by these cruel poachers.
Mourning for their family and friends,
The fun for them had never begun, so I can't even
say that it has come to an end.

We must help and save these wonders of the
planet,
Let's help save their home, their natural habitat.

Or we will have to bid goodbye to these noble elephant boys and girls,
Goodbye to the largest land dwellers that roamed the Earth.

Diah Patel (11)

Our World

Caring for the environment,
I carefully pick up litter,
Be nice to this world and don't be bitter,
Animals all need our help,
Do a good deed on this day,
Be the best eco hero you can!

Don't destroy terrific trees,
We need oxygen,
A lovely fresh breeze.

Let's all help to stop pollution,
Trying to find a solution,
A wonderful idea struck in my brain,
Why not write a poem?
To stop this nonsense, you see!
I'm only ten,
But I hope you listen,
For the final time, stop this pollution!

This is our future,
Lovely and clean,
Beautiful as it can be,

Joyful animals merrily dancing,
Birds singing melodies,
All the litter into the bin,
People happily wondering how this world became
so super clean!

We can all make a big difference!

Anvi Mahajan (10)

The Billowing Breeze (Ode To Kew Gardens)

The billowing breeze
Shifts the flourishing trees with ease.

The more people in it
The hive will hum a pattern
And no other building
Can make that happen.

In the lily house
The tadpoles are unseen with camouflage
And the big question is how small
Is their entourage.

In the palm house the plants love water
And there is more water than a quarter.

The Latin name for an oak is quercus
And it's not complicated on purpose.

The pitcher plants
Have their height advantage
Higher than where lily pads were planted.

The bamboo shoots
Are the fastest growing grass
And their outsides
Are as hard as brass.

The trees whisper where the winds blow
And what they say no one knows
But if you hear a bamboo sneeze
You have awoken the billowing breeze.

Maya Pal (8)

That Time Of Year

When that time of year comes,
And when the beautiful flowers bloom,
The blinding sun half submerged in the clouds,
Sometimes it rains, sometimes it doesn't,
Imagine that time of year.

When that time of year comes,
And when the trees are as green as grass,
The weather is blazing,
Sunburns are to be seen,
Imagine that time of year.

When that time of year comes,
And the gorgeous leaves fall,
The sunset colours just make me laugh,
Some are ripped some are not,
Imagine that time of year.

When that time of year comes,
And the big gusts of wind hit the trees,
The snow drifting in the air,
Snowflakes come down with ease,
Imagine that time of year.

What comes next?
What's in the future?
Will it be left unknown?
We don't know.

Arisha Rahman (8)

Make Nature An Adventure

Rescue the animals
And creatures in the sea
We can all do this if you listen to me
Chuck that tin in the purple bin, it's a win!

Recycle your plastics
You'll be fantastic
If you don't it will be drastic.

After junk modelling
Recycle your paper and card
Pop it in the blue bag
It isn't that hard.

Look after your environment
And make the world a better place
It will be ace.

Smoke in the air
Let people be aware
Let's find a solution

To stop the pollution
And find a conclusion.

Make nature an adventure
Recycling is fun
If we all do our bit
We all have won.

Mia Thomas (10)

Climate Change

My name is Elias and I'm here to say,
Climate change is being experienced today!
It is not natural, so you see,
Help the Earth with so much glee!
You might be capable of getting an electric car,
A Porsche, a Peugeot or a Tesla!
Our world is still overheating,
But humans are sitting around, beef they are eating!
Our world used to be so fantastic,
But now our seas are congested with plastic!
We are burning fossil fuels severely fast,
Will coal, oil and natural gases even last?
Even the smallest types of children can help the problem,
So don't be so extremely solemn!
It's easy to do, don't be in denial,
Reduce, reuse and recycle!

Elias De-Lisser (8)

The Animals Of Earth

The bountiful earth so much it gives,
Four seasons blow by like a rhythmic parade,
Shunning animals to their bunkers,
Spring bears fruit to the trees,
Winter smears snow across the land,
Offering a hand to the animals' faint,
Summer breathing a fiery inferno throughout the Earth,
Shrivelling most plants dead,
Autumn dying the leaves red,
Biting winds dive overhead,
But which creature affects the seasons most,
Not lions, tigers or leopards nor
Whales, eagles or sharks
The most destructive of them all is
Undoubtedly, the humans
Vile, Earth destroyers,
Stinking world polluters they are
Us animals have no control.

Paul Wang (9)

Stop Pollution

The sea is getting trashed,
And it's also getting bashed.
When you pollute it's bad,
And it's not at all rad.

So that's why we must save the Earth,
From all the litter in the ocean.
But if you don't all the creatures die,
And then you will have to say goodbye.

If I were you, I wouldn't waste time,
'Cause you must stop this great crime.
Come together, join hands,
All of us to form a band.

If you're a vegan it's also good,
Not to get the animals in a mood.
Save the sea, if you do what I say,
Then you can have a break and play.

Now save the fishes,
It will grant your wishes.
If you're very keen,
The sea would be very clean.

Anaelechi Amaechi (9)

Reduce, Reuse, Recycle, Repeat

Reduce, reuse, recycle, repeat,
Covered in rubbish from heads to our feet,
Look up in the sky, see midnight's aura,
Look down at your feet, see the fauna and flora,
Stare left, glare right,
Everywhere you look there's more rubbish in sight,
But among these escalating towers you may find,
A way to find hope and peace of mind,
A chance, a possibility, a way,
For Mother Nature, we cannot betray,
She gave us our planet,
Plastic waste, we must ban it!
Yet all this remains a dream,
Where we all wish to be coated in foliar leaves,
We're still blanketed in darkness, heads to our feet,
Reduce, reuse, recycle, repeat.

Isabella Samples (10)

Even When The World Was Green

The woods and forests lend a hand,
Letting children run around the land,
Don't just repay it by dropping litter,
For bird, fish, animal or critter,
And gorgeous trees that let us breathe,
The world upon its back it heaves,
And, I don't think it's fair to see,
People killing them in front of me,
We used to have a good supply,
But it's disappearing before one's eye,
And across the world, there are many cities,
Full of nature's misery, and human pities,
Whenever I walked around the earth,
I saw plants growing on fresh new turf,
Now the thing that's striking me,
Is the disappearing bumblebee,
This very thing was plain to see,
Even when the world was green.

Logan Hay (11)

The Earth's Destruction

The forests are gone.
The air is heavy.
The sky is black.
Ice has melted.
Pandas and polar bears are gone.

Water's polluters by litter and waste.
Oceans and lakes lie barren.
All wildlife gone and forgotten.

Wars have started.
Pollution is destroying the Earth.
The Earth is dying all because of man.

Mankind have destroyed all that is good.
Soon the world will be gone, gone, gone...
Because of man.

But we can help stop this
Preventing further pollution, destruction
Deforestation and loss of wildlife.
We can help the Earth recover
Starting now by doing our part.

Amy White Fox (12)

What Were We Thinking?

What were we thinking?
Don't you know this is not good?
To climate change and pollution,
And cutting down all that wood.

What were we thinking?
Can we go back now?
All those poor trees
We're hopefully going to get through, somehow.

What were we thinking?
Oh, my oh my,
Global warming and reduced wildlife
Let's all give a great sigh.

All that nature waiting to be explored,
Ruined by all those selfish people,
Always waiting to be adored.

Why don't we make a change?
Be the one who stands out,
What were we thinking?
So let's hear you shout!

Isabelle Evans (10)

I Will Become A Tree Ambassador

I will become a Tree Ambassador,
And the Earth I will save.
I'll plant multiple trees,
Help animals in need,
For the Earth I will save.

I will become a Tree Ambassador,
And the Earth I will save.
I'll proclaim my word,
And I will be heard,
For the Earth I will save.

I will become a Tree Ambassador,
And the Earth I will save.
I'll stop global warming
Whilst feeling like soaring
For the Earth I will save.

I will become a Tree Ambassador,
And the Earth I will save.
Stick around and see,

The Tree Ambassador I will be,
For the Earth I will save!

Janna Oyedeji (10)

Don't Eat Meat

Mr Pig likes to dig,
Mr Pig lives on the moor.
Mr Pig is a boar,
But pollution changed his gig.

Mr Pig had a chore,
To roam the world for small truffles.
That's when he got into scuffles,
Because he wanted more.

So he leapt, he took flight,
He cried out loud, full of might.
So he caught a light,
And made a wave so full of fright.

Now, dear friends, let's be kind,
Pigs feel joy and pain.
And just like us, they love to play,
And should not be just food to grind.

So let's choose a meal that's kind,
And leave Mr Pig and his friends behind.

Velarian Hutchcroft (7)

Facts About Climate Change

O ur remaining carbon budget is tiny

U sing different stock feeds can help to reduce farming's contribution to climate change

R educing the amount of electricity generated from coal and gas will aid climate change.

P eople have already caused 1.07c of warming

L and use change and deforestation contribute to 15% of carbon emissions every year

A ir pollution is both good and bad

N ASA found that 2010-2019 was the hottest decade every recorded

E xtreme heat events have become more frequent and severe

T he ocean absorbs most of the heat we produce.

Lily Robinson (5)

The Ocean Is Calling!

The ocean is calling,
It is calling for help!
Pompous people, stop littering!
The junk is too much for her.
World of the ocean prays for help.
Coral is breaking by the minute, time is ticking.
Stop now! Stop these oil spills and noise pollution
Which is killing the whales and dolphins that dwell
in it.
The little fish hide or feast on the yeeted plastic,
Only to tragically die!
You are hurting Mother Sea, you see,
So you must stop these evil, sea-littering deeds.
The squishy, mushy seaweed even dies,
Of these eco safe lies.
The ocean is calling,
It is calling for help!

Akshath Bandreddi (10)

What If...?

We're the guardians of the Earth so wild,
What if we care for it as our own child?
What happens to the Earth as the pollution grows bigger?
We're chopping down forests and trees with humongous diggers,
We can't count the resources we're stealing,
How can we transform our efforts to bring healing?

What if the Earth could talk, what would she say?
It can heal if you start today,
Start planting, not plundering forests and flowers,
Start doing the things within our power.
Stop kidding ourselves, stop putting it off,
There's no Planet B, enough is enough.

Georgia Kirby (8)

Gaia's Tale

I am your Earth,
Your luscious green turf,
Bat me and beat me,
But don't try to please me,
You have ruined my dream,
Your soft, emerald sheen,
Why well...
Machines and machines!
You make these awful beasts,
For some create steam,
And that is just mean!
You chop down my nice trees,
To make room for these...
Machines!
The CO2
That you produce,
Goes off to the atmosphere,
Really it's true!
It makes it all jet-black,
Instead of blue!

Landscapes will go,
Plants will go,
Animals will go,
And gradually so will you.

Zoe Wakelin (10)

Rain

The trees so tall,
All their leaves fall,
When you look down,
You see red, yellow, green and brown,

The sky so blue,
Is where the birds flew,
But now there is no water,
And the clouds seem shorter,
The rain used to get all the fame,
It was never lame,

The grass so green,
Is really supreme,
The summer months have passed,
And gone by really fast,

The flowers are wilting,
And the daffodils groaning,
Because there's no rain,
It all seems so plain,

When we think rain is bad,
Rain makes the plants glad.

Millie Needleman (10)

Treasured Earth

Wind blowing wild,
Foxes running fast,
People wondering how to care for a world so vast.

Why do we litter?
It's really bad behaviour,
Wouldn't it be better to be a world saviour?

Think of the animals living in the sea so blue,
To save them we need help from you,
Follow these rules and you'll know what to do...

Reduce,
Reuse,
Recycle.

Nature is beautiful and it's living too,
But the creatures we love,
Are becoming so few!

So, the next time you have some rubbish to throw,
Remember we need all this wildlife to grow!

Wind blowing wild,
Foxes running fast,
People wondering how long the Earth will last.

Jessica Ann McCartney (9)

Nature

Nature is a place full of animals and plants,
If you look closely, you might find some ants.
When it comes to nature, there are lots you can see,
There are different types of species, even for a tree.

Nature is full of surprises, and I mean more than I can think,
So, ask someone who explores, and they can probably link.
Nature is a place completely splattered in green,
As exploring nature is better than a magazine.

There aren't only plants, but animals too,
So, if you try to list them all, there is a lot to unscrew.
Jungles, waterfalls, there's lots to discover,
But be careful, there are snakes undercover!

Farah Karim (10)

The Jungle

Jungle, jungle, the vines are nice and long.
Jungle, jungle, the berries are on the vine's tongue.
Jungle, jungle, they make me relax.
Jungle, jungle, there's nothing it lacks,
Tree frogs have packs and packs.
So, don't cut trees down,
The ecosystem helps us at a busy town.
The jungle helps our ecosystem.
There are so many plants, I can't list them.
In the jungle, there are some tasks you can bungle
The jungle is amazing.
Just like a rainforest, they are bracing.
The rainforest is full of animals
Some of them are mammals.
The jungle has lots of surprises.
Hiding in bushes, there may be prizes.

Oluwatamilore Fajorin (8)

Act Now

C limate change is happening all the time
L iving animals are dying
I t may kill us too
M ankind is to blame
A rctic is getting warmer, ice is melting
T ime to change our ways
E ventually, there will be nothing left of our world.

C ould you help?
H elp by riding a bike or scooter to school or even walk
A ct now before time runs out
N ow we have no second chances
G et involved before it's too late
E veryone needs to get together now! Everyone needs to care.

Esther Blakeway (7)

Explorers Galore

Beneath the canopy, gloomy and dark,
Towering trees covered in bark,
This is where the secrets are found,
From uppermost branches, to deep on the ground.

Soaring winged predators roam the skies,
In the canopy tree frogs hunt flies,
A dozy sloth hangs from a tree,
Cheeky monkeys howling with glee.

Jaguars sneakily hunting their prey,
The tail of a lemur showing the way,
Scarlet macaws swoop as a flock,
A rainbow of colours running amok.

Here is more life than anyone knows,
Here in the rainforest,
Energy flows.

Ellis Woodward (9)

The Forest Of Life

Don't cut down the trees, there will be nowhere for
the bees
Won't somebody think of the bees?
Or the monkeys having nowhere to hang in the
breeze
What will the koalas have for tea
If there are no branches on the trees?
Where will the parrots perch
Without their special rainforest church?
Where will the cheetah hunt their prey?
Stop chopping down the trees today!
There will be no shady trees for boars.
All the animals' skin will just get sore.
Where will we all go for tours?
There will be no rainforest for the wildlife's paws.

Ella Elderfield (9)

Reality Has Spoken

Animals are being forced out of their homes,
Just because you won't hand wash your clothes,
Sea levels are rising,
But all we care about is our rising signs,
The Antarctic is melting due to global warming,
And we can't even heat our houses,
380 tonnes of plastic goes into the ocean every
year,
And that isn't the least of our fear,
School shootings, we are fully prepared,
We should be able to keep our classrooms aired,
By opening windows and doors,
We shouldn't have to rely on the norms,
Why has humanity ruined the world?

Ella Wozny (11)

The Wise Old Oak

The wise old oak dwells in a forest right now,
He lives alongside many creatures and an owl,
Every day he's getting much more rings,

Which means he is old and quite often he brings:
Insects and mammals and beetles and grubs,
Seen all around him are lots of fox cubs,
Every branch on his tree is covered in buds.

Oh no! But what's this?
Little people are destroying such a bright merry
bliss!
Days going by, half the forest is down!

Over there, by those hills, you can see a small
town.
A combination of nature and humans can't fit,
Keeping in mind there is still time to change it...

Imogen Kay (8)

Endangered Animals

E lephants,
N orthern white rhinos,
D on't get me started, don't you know?
A frican lion,
N o, no, no!
G reen turtle,
E urasian badger,
R ocky mountain locust,
E very one of them to go,
D odo, a bird that was extinct a long time ago.

A frican elephant,
N o more please,
I t's so sad, jeez!
M adagascar fish,
A ll these are endangered animals,
L osing them,
S o many species, help them, please!

Olivia Ann Mitchell (9)

Be Eco-Friendly

S ave our planet, we need to act,
A worrying time and that's a fact,
V ery much of our world is full of litter,
E veryone needs to keep the planet fitter.

O ur world is depending on us,
U nless we act, bad things we'll see,
R emember there's no Planet B.

P ollution in the air,
L itter everywhere,
A nimals are suffering,
N ow is the time to do something,
E ven a little will go a long way,
T ime to act, I'm here to say!

Sophie Armstrong (8)

Nature Is All Around

Nature is all around us,
From the colossal trees, beautiful seas and luscious leaves,
To the flowers, grass that cows devour and wheat which gives us flour,
And everything in-between.
Nature is natural.
Nature is beautiful.
Nature is everything we need.
Please do your best to keep the Earth clean.
Please do your best not to cut down trees.
Please do your best not to tear leaves.
Please do your best not to eat berries.
Please do your best to put my mind at ease.
Please do your best to remember nature is all around us.

Jayden Klu

One World, One Nature

Brushing like waterfalls
Tears streaming down
Extinction, pollution the
Climate - we drown.

One world, one nature

Another tree fell,
More nature is lost
Look at the world
And what we have lost.

One world, one nature

We look at our phones
And turn a blind eye
Thunder, chaos and panic lights up the sky.

One world, one nature

Everyone, come together
We are in this together

Let's save the world
And make it our goal.

My world, my nature.

Evelyn Shipway (13)

Respect

The grace, the awe, the wonder,
Of animals, big cats and all,
The sight makes me grow fonder,
Of all creatures big or small.

I stand enraged,
At some trapped and caged,
Some that poachers kill,
Causing destruction, until...

The strong arm of the law,
Is what they saw,
When something cruel becomes illegal,
It will only stop some people.

Together we can gaze at their beauty,
Together we can save them from threat,
That is our duty,
Otherwise, we'll live in regret.

Appreciate their magic,
Make it automatic,

To respect all creation
For the good of the next generation.

Joel Bance (10)

Saving The Seals

My poem starts in Antarctica, home to the seal
The reason I love them is that they look like they've
had too many meals
They lie on the ground, they are grey, white and fat
Just like Beau Beau, my big, round, fat cat
Seals need ice for somewhere to play and eat
But the ice is melting so killer whales see the seals
as meat
We need to stop the planet getting warmer by
doing simple things at home
I now take showers instead of baths, I turn the
lights off and now have my own recycle zone
I end my poem hoping everyone will think of seals
because climate change is very real.

Andromeda Bellamy (8)

Green Intruder

An adorable bluebird settled on a tree
Whilst a tiny, shy mouse crept on all the leaves
The grass felt greener than ever before
Covering up the forest floor
A human throws a plastic intruder
They couldn't be ever so ruder
Not a thought for the harm it will cause
They carried on walking, didn't stop to pause
The wildlife gasped at the danger ahead
"That's ruining our habitat, we'll be homeless,"
they said.
So humans, remember our planet is shared
It would be a beautiful home if everyone cared.

Olive Nell Allington-King (8)

Down By The River

Down by the river
Where the hot sun glows
I put on my hat
With its colourful bows

Down by the river
Some ducks are having fun
They squibble and squabble
And then they start to run

Down by the river
I hear a gentle creak
I think it's a mouse
It goes squeak, squeak, squeak

Down by the river
I touch a willow tree
It wraps me in its branches
And it comforts me

Down by the river
Yes, I do love it here

I want to stay forever
Or be very near.

Ella Lucy Dharmadasa (8)

Nature

If you don't want to bungle,
Help me save the jungle.
Stop cutting the trees to make more grain,
You're hurting the Earth and causing pain.
These forests are living and catching the rain,
Cutting them down results in empty gain.
We want to see lots more green,
And stop the greedy people being mean.
If you want to keep your conscience clean,
Stop killing animals or they will be unseen.
Don't lose your mind,
So you can help me be kind.
We are all fearful,
To see you destroy a place so beautiful.

Aurora Walker (9)

Powerless Pandas!

Us solitary panda bears are quite particular, as we don't like to socialise,
We prefer the quiet life amongst the bamboo, which is our favourite food,
We have the perfect coat to camouflage, so we don't attract the wrong eyes,
If we don't get enough to eat, it puts us in a really dreadful mood,
So please stop cutting down our forest, because we'd like to emphasise,
We need at least a month to move, before we can leave our brood,
What's up with you humans anyway? Can't you empathise?
Leaving us poor pandas powerless and homeless is awfully rude!

Ayesha Birmingham (10)

Go Green

Global warming is taking place,
And the polar bears don't have a safe space.
The poor creatures, oh so sad,
Let's stop polluting so they don't feel bad.

Poor little tortoise, we've done them some harm,
Let's keep the sea clean and calm.

Refill and reuse all the plastic,
It would be so fantastic
When we see the dramatic change
We made between our range.

Let's all make it possible,
As a team we are unstoppable.
Let's make a solution,
To reduce the pollution.

Aashi Karia (11)

Our Environment

P oor animals dying at sea,

O n the bottom of the deep blue sea, there is always a piece of plastic that never leaves,

L eft for animals to scramble their way through,

L andfall giants increasing their size, bigger and bigger,

U ntil one day their lives change,

T rees crying in agony just like the animals,

I nvisible car fumes making air unbreakable,

O n top of the ginormous sea, floats harmful things to animals,

N o way should animals be treated like this, or our Earth.

Billie-Marie Perry (11)

The Wild Woods

For going in the woods,
People always say it's nice
Although I had my doubts,
I still followed their advice
Closing the door on my way out,
I started to walk but heard a shout!
It was a person,
I was certain
One of the countless victims
Of the pure venom
Of what people called good
But was actually terrible woods!
I continued my 'stroll',
But I felt that my soul
Was being set on fire
Like an old, deflated tyre
I saw an animal,
Really vicious and tyrannical
It was causing terror
It was really clever

It liked squashing
It loved brainwashing.

Ishaan Singh (8)

How To Save The Earth

When we go to the park, don't litter on the ground because
It will be found on the ocean floor.
When we go to the beach, don't leave plastic bags behind because
Tortoises will dine on it and die.
When we go shopping, don't buy plastic bags because
They will be dumped into the sea after.
When it is summer, don't use an air conditioner to cool down because
It will create CO_2 and it will cause cruel wildfires and extreme weather.
When you buy a notebook, chose the recycled paper because
We need trees to collect the CO_2 to provide us oxygen.

Yeuk Lam Ha (9)

Have You Ever?

Have you ever seen a beach looking oh so down?
Plastic and rubbish spreading all around.

Have you ever seen a city not very pretty?
For an example, New York City.

Have you ever seen animals being hurt?
Don't blame them, they think plastic is dessert.

Plastic bags blowing in the wind,
Mind you, they should've been binned.

Before I go I have one thing to say.
Look after our world, it's done nothing wrong,
Don't throw rubbish, let's keep the planet strong.

Gracie Laughton (8)

Saviour Of Nature

The forest is a sacred place,
It is surrounded by a quiet space,
Though it may be dark,
If you look closely, you'll see a slight spark,
Take the time to explore and you'll find the
outdoors really ace;

Trees are helpers of the Earth,
They help with many things such as births,
They protect our land,
Just by stretching a mere hand,
Never forget what trees are worth;

Once we had a beautiful land,
But now it's not so grand,
We all have flaws,
But it's never too late to lay down the saws,
If we all take a stand, we can save our land.

Shaina France-Scotland (9)

Melting Polar Ice Caps

The satellites out in space
Can see the devastation happening in the ocean place.

The Earth is heating up like a giant radiator,
And Antarctica is melting like a giant ice cream left out in the sun.

The wildlife are becoming homeless
And there is less floating ice for them to rest on.

What will happen to them?
Where will they go?
What will happen if there is no more snow for them to nest on?

We need to stop contributing to the problem of constant harmful pollution
And work together to find a safe and speedy solution.

Kaleia Peres (7)

It's Just Not Fair

Unfortunately, some unlucky animals are in
danger,
Sadly, some can't run around in nature,
And even have an adventure.
But if one of them survived they would...

Breathe in fresh air and if they're lucky
Maybe even meet a kind grizzly bear!

That's what makes them happy!
Devastatingly, the unlucky ones have to live in
terrible conditions such as...
Choking, misty air,
No trees to climb!
Some are even
Trapped inside.

It's just not fair.

Lacey Cameron (10)

I Love Nature

I love nature
Nature is really interesting because,
Some animals are creepy crawlies and others are
soft to touch
Nature is really exciting because,
Ladybirds are my favourite as they have black
spots
Nature is really interesting because,
Spiders make really nice webs, and they catch flies
in the net
Nature is really fun because,
I get to put my wellies on and splash in the muddy
puddles
Nature is beautiful because
There are lots of different plants
Nature is noisy because
Lots of birds are singing.

Yuvraj Minhas (6)

Earth's Pain

Plastic and litter make the Earth cry.
Pollution and smoke float up and choke the sky.
Angry axes torture the terrified trees,
Nature's destruction causes pain to even bees.

Wildlife animals are slowly losing their habitats,
All our plants and ponds are facing attacks.
Sad seas give a deep groan,
As they get weaker with all the rubbish thrown.

The planet gets gloomier, as many lives fade,
Let's support our Earth and provide it aid.
We must give the environment a chance to survive,
To save the world, we must strive!

Nusayba Ahmed (11)

The Environment Poem

The environment matters as it is where we live,
If we can work together we can give.

The world a better chance of surviving,
We can make the changes now to make it thriving.

Global warming is making the world hotter,
We need to take care of all the creatures including
the otter.

Pollution is harmful to the air, water and land,
You can even find litter in the sand.

Deforestation is purposely cutting down trees,
If we want fresh fruit and veggies we need the
bees.

If we make these changes now,
We can make the world wow.

Logan Fullerton (7)

It's My Earth Too!

It's my Earth too, I tell them,
It's my Earth too, I say,
Because the actions of the adults,
Are damaging our world every day.

What can I do to help? I say,
What can I do to protect?
Because our precious Planet Earth
Deserves lots of respect.

Nobody said I could make a change,
Because I am just a child,
But I know I must help save the planet
To save our forests, our wilds.

Reduce, reuse and recycle,
We need to now more than ever,
Because if we save our precious planet
Nobody would've thought we said never.

Lilly Newman (10)

Crisp Evening

As the night falls around me,
The evening chills, it cools and turns crisp,
Wet, tenacious leaves grip to my back,
I lie down in tranquillity yet,
No silence to break,
I gaze up at the crescent moon,
So near while so far,
The stars twinkle above,
A splash and a sputter as I rise up from the ground,
I trudge through the woods,
So perfect and green but, I must arrive home,
The nature calls me in like a siren with its gaze,
Maybe I shall rest and simply dream here.

Taylor Hotchkiss (11)

Make It Greener

The Earth once was beautiful, colourful and bright,
You and me should stop polluting, it's really not right.
The sky is changing colour, it's full of gas and smoke,
We have to stop this now because it's making us all choke!

Everyone, grab gloves, hurry and be quick!
Throwing plastic rubbish is making the Earth sick!

Animals, trees and plants are dying, all of them are sad and crying.
We have to make our planet cleaner, stop throwing rubbish and make it greener.

Ayla Tuffaha (6)

Don't Pollute

D on't throw rubbish on the floor
O therwise animals will die
N ever damage the Earth by polluting
T o save our planet put rubbish in the bin

P ollution is bad, now do you see why?
O nly throw rubbish in the bin
L eaving rubbish on the floor is illegal
L et animals live a good life
U nder the sea is where your rubbish goes
T rash goes in the bin not outside the bin
E veryone, follow these rules.

Jimmy Smith (8)

We Are The Solution

I've been thinking,
That vehicles' fumes are stinking,
And there's plastic in the waves,
Due to the way litterers behave.
Have you ever thought
That the plastic that you've bought
Could end up in the sea
Polluting it for you and me?
No? Well, you should see,
Next time you're by the sea,
If you can do some litter picking,
Because the clock is ticking!
How are *you* going to make a contribution
To finding a solution to pollution?

Rosie Barnes (10)

Save Our Planet

This is a poem about rubbish in the sea,
Although the sea looks as beautiful as can be.

If we take a closer look you shall see
That we should save our sea.

Think about all the fish
That can't be seen stuck in the deep blue sea.

Please save our planet,
Little by little,
Recycle your waste,
To not let animals taste,
Plastic or paper,
That's not right
Because you might impact our seas.
Make a move today
To save tomorrow.

Ava Hutton (9)

The Earth Is Watching

Why waste half your dinner?
Why discard your tea?
Why throw anything away
Just because it's free?

Why leave taps on to run?
Why leave on the light?
Why grab all our kind Earth gives?
It's just not polite!

Why tramp over flowers?
Why pull leaves off trees?
Why leave litter on the beach to clutter up seas?

I wouldn't tease our Earth,
Or be too impolite.
If it sees you trash its treats,
It may turn around and bite!

Safiya Khan (11)

It Starts With A Seed

It starts with a seed,
I know what it needs.
Some growing space,
The polytunnel is the place.
Not too cold or too hot,
Plant with soil in a pot.

With water it will germinate,
Before it ends up on your plate.
Roots, a stem and then a flower,
Growing food is a superpower.
Give it lots of sunlight,
The fruit is a lovely sight.

Harvest time is here,
The best time of the year.
Homegrown food is healthy,
Sell some to get wealthy.
Growing food is really fun,
It's good for the environment and everyone.

Daisy Duffield (8)

What I Need To Say To You

I tower over you
Proudly,
But you just trundle by,
Like a figure in the darkness
You don't notice me at all...
You don't seem to care,
But throughout your whole lifetime I've been caring for you;
By providing you with the oxygen you need to survive.

Our kind is dying out dangerously,
While you sit back and relax
Time is running out.

We've stopped working together;
Your selfish, stupid attitude has brought us to our knees,
But... the last laugh will be on you;
If I go, you go too.

Phoebe Mace (8)

To Save The World

When you see rubbish on the streets,
And the air smells like pollution,
While you keep on coughing and coughing,
Don't forget there is a solution.

There's something everyone can do,
To keep everyone safe,
To keep fresh the air we breathe,
And keep the plants healthy.

Help clean up a beach,
Or recycle bottles and cans,
It doesn't have to be a lot,
Learn about the problems we each face.

We can take our part,
To help Mother Nature,
Else there will be no planet,
To live on anymore...

Shreya Sapkota (7)

Save The Forest

Forests are burning,
Trees are turning,
A magical, mysterious place turned into,
A dull, dark place!
So why are you killing?
When you are supposed to be saving,
You are destroying wildlife,
When you are supposed to have pride.
I was devastated to see the beautiful forest has
been knocked down,
Seeing the beautiful, peaceful animals suffer made
me frown.
People can't breathe without trees.
So don't ruin any more, please!
Stop being destructive!
When you are supposed to be positive!

Lucia Palmer (9)

Our Environment

I love my environment,
Pollution free,
Squirrels happily running up trees,
The beach air so fresh,
Sand beneath my feet,
Not a cloud in the sky, so peaceful,
A plastic bottle washed ashore,
Why hurt our animals and pollute the sea?
Everyone should recycle,
And keep everything clean,
I see a seal happily swimming around,
The sand is rough to touch,
Sea air as fresh as a daisy,
Please love our environment and keep it clean.

Oliver Morgan (8)

Pick Up Your Rubbish

Don't you want to make the world cleaner?
Pick up your rubbish, making it greener.

Come on, let's make the world a better place,
Pick up your rubbish, let's make some space.

Finding better ways to dispose of waste,
Pick up your rubbish, move with haste.

Only we can make the change,
Pick up your rubbish, let's rearrange.

Keep on going and don't hesitate,
Share this with others, to help educate.

Bobby Fisher (9)

What Am I?

I am endangered, which means there are not many
of us to be found.
Builders digging new roads mean we have to
move.
This is hard for us because it's difficult to find food.
Climate change is bad for us because we live on
the ground.
Litter is a problem because it's all around.
It's dangerous and puts us in a bad mood,
When people throw their litter, it's really rude.
When we step on litter, it makes a scary sound.
Look after this endangered, precious planet right
now!

Maryam Ibrahim (6)

Mama Duck

Mama Duck and Duckling went looking for lunch,
Mama thought she found some bread,
But it was a piece of litter instead,
It choked her as she began to nibble and munch,
Now Baby Duck's all alone with no mummy,
All because you simply won't use a bin or recycle,
It's super important for our safety and survival,
Don't throw rubbish in the sea so we don't get it in our beaks,
There's no time at all to wait,
So, let's save our planet before it's too late!

Adam Umar (7)

Please Save The Trees

Please save the trees,
They are homes to
Monkeys, birds and bees;

Please save the trees,
They clean our air,
So we really should care;

Please save the trees,
They need help right away,
They've been waiting day to day;

Please save the trees,
We all know it's wrong,
We all know it all along,
But not enough seems to be done;

Please save the trees,
We need them for Christmas
And Christmas is fabulous;

Let's save our trees,
There's still hope,
We can still cope.

Zoe Tsitouridis (8)

Nothing

Nothing, just nothing
A void of dead emptiness
Why?
The trees like dominos falling one by one with their
last beat of a heart
Gone. Done
Nothing left. Never again
Ended
Animals fled their once-luscious, vibrant homes
No, why just why?
Breathless trees
Groan and moan
Just no
Do we want it like this?
Do we want this?
Plants and trees motionless
Animals left devastated
Do we want nothing, just nothing?

Madeleine Heap (9)

Help Me Live

I help you breathe
So please, don't chop me
I provide fruit as the birds hoot.
I don't complain when you lie on me to read your book.

So in return, I don't want to be burnt.
You should have learnt not to harm me.
Because I'm just an innocent tree.
Please, try your best to save me.
They'll lose their nature.
I'm good for the environment.
I'm not ready for retirement.
Please don't cut me
So the Earth will still be green.

Sincerely,
The oak tree.

Michelle Akadiri

Perilous Pollution

Perilous pollution, created by us,
You are a treasure chest that is dirty,
You trap creatures cruelly, no mercy,
Ravenous for plastic and extremely unworthy,

Perilous pollution, created by us,
You are a something that makes us unease,
You reek of deadly, disgusting disease,
You're a bad thing, the world agrees,

Perilous pollution, created by us,
You are a tsunami of rubbish wrecking nature,
You contaminate and cause danger,
And slaughter like a cruel, fearsome stranger

Isabella Nikolov (9)

Fifty Of You

You, slimy bumblebee
With marble eyes as clear as water
Your legs like frozen jelly sticks with a bit of lemon
sizzle
Your silky mouth is a boomerang
Your darting tongue as straight as a line
Your patterns are silent strokes from a striped
cheetah's fur
What a pity not as many people get to witness
your beauty
Since your population are like small gnomes living
inside a guitar
I would travel all the way to Australian bogs to see
you,
Such a rare southern corroboree frog.

Carrie Wang (11)

Trees With Breeze, The Breath Of An Animal

Trees are swaying as trash is flying
People don't know
How much the Earth is dying.
Fires are spreading
Making animals lose their homes with a drone
And cars make the air toxic to breathe through our lungs.
Flies and bugs are not looking after the plants
'Cause people are killing them thinking they're venomous.
Icebergs are melting, making the sea erupt
Making cities go into the deep of the cold, icy, salty water.

Scarlett Impey (10)

Our Planet

I stood and watched the world go by,
The air so damaged it could kill a fly.
The guilt of all the things we've done,
We're being warmed by our precious sun!
We need to end this dangerous act,
All come together to make this pact...

A pact to stop plastic.
A pact to stop fumes.
A pact to stop straws.
A pact to save our planet.

So tomorrow, walk out your door,
And please aspire to be more!
More to the planet.
More to the Earth.
More to me.
More to you.

Alice Formoy (13)

The Oak Tree

In a park,
In the green,
Stood the oak tree,
Three ages old,
Nature's history book.

And when the litter got stuck in its branches,
It still stood there,
Strong as a lion,

When a virus came,
It still stood there,
Gazing at the city,

When children threw pebbles at it,
It still stood there,
Being the tree it always had been,

But when the man came running with the axe,
It did not still stand,
It gazed up at the world

As a weak,
Hopeless,
Tree stump.

Muna White (11)

Save The World!

The world is big, the world is wide,
We need to stand together side by side,
The animals are coming to extinction
Jungle, Arctic and sea.
Let's change the world, this is not the way it should be!
Stop littering, let's all come to peace.
The trees are falling like my heart,
Why are you doing this, they have done no harm?
The ice in the Arctic is breaking so fast,
If you keep doing this, the animals will never last.
Let's save the world!

Thailula Thompson (10)

Veganism

V eganism is a philosophy and a way of living,

E at no meat,

G reat meat substitutes;

A re tempeh, seitan, tofu, black beans, lentils and jackfruit.

N o testing on animals for soap.

I s ridiculed, mocked and dismissed.

S uper vegan actors protesting for animal rights.

M eet Earth man-made from trees and refuge, he'd clear plastic from the seas and stop animal slaughter...

George Frank Gamble (9)

Environment

From years to years our Earth remains the same.
Oh no, what a shame!
From cardboard, plastic, paper and rubbish
Nobody reads leaflets that are published!

Millions of animals are harmed
Is this not a warning alarm?
Air pollution or water contamination,
Let's get rid of this exploitation!

Bring a change to this environment,
Let's not have an argument!
Everybody wants a good Earth
So let's make a change today in a rightful way!

Tvisha Suchak (10)

My World

M ust we cut down the trees? No

Y ou are eco-friendly! Yes

W ould you like to plant some trees with me? Sure

O kay, let's also do some litter picking! Yes

R ound the world there is a 'bad blanket', making the world overheat. We must stop this. Together!

L ower your energy use, turn off those screens! Now

D rive less often and walk with me in my world.

Edward McFarland (7)

Plastic In The Ocean

The ocean is the home of a lot of fish
And that's a reason to not put in rubbish
Because of all the plastic, the fish are dying
So when you go shopping, fish is not what you're
buying
If we recycle
Things will be sensible
If everyone does their part
The world will be a piece of art
Put bottles in the recycling bin
And also plastic and tins
Save the seas
Pull up your sleeves.

Kushy Kaur (10)

Please Save Me

I'm the Earth,
I feel everything, litter all over me,
Trees falling all around me,
Ignored by many,
Animals beg for help from me,
I have no arms, mouth or legs,
It's not up to me but to you.

However, some animals are safe,
In their habitats,
Because of some people that,
Show nurture, care and love,
So take action,
Save the animals,
Save the environment,
Save me.

Ameena Adil (7)

My Nature Poem

I am not dead, I am alive
I grow and grow until I show
I am everywhere but you sometimes ignore me
I am green and the brightest colours of all
I have roots, a stem and a petal or two
I am beautiful and gorgeous
I am great and kind
I am to a community, a kingdom
I make you live for as long as possible
I live where you live
I watch you play all day
I take care of you, you should take care of me
I am tall or small
I am your life energy.

Archie Mould (11)

Mother Earth

I am Mother Earth
Big, blue, bright, beautiful,
A tiny dot in the universe,
Full of life.
Home to many vibrant, vivid creatures.

I need your help, help me
I am sad, I am choking, I feel uncared for.
You can save me.
Forests, oceans and air need care

It's not too late,
Stop throwing rubbish
Stop polluting the ocean
Stop driving petrol or diesel cars
Stop cutting trees down

Please, save me
I would really appreciate it
Please.

Mason Sejpal (9)

Tropical Wild

Once there were no bees,
So God grew the trees.
Wildlife thrived around the earth,
Later came the human birth.
Vines grew everywhere,
Babbling brooks, mountains here and there.
Glistening vines above the canal,
Blooming flowers on the chaparral.
Nature cottages all around,
With some still waiting to be found.
And this is the topical wild,
Where everyone enjoys like a child.

Luqman Ahmad (9)

Save The Turtles

T orturing turtles, I feel mad,
U nder the ocean the turtles are sad,
R ise up and make a change,
T o stop the world from staying the same,
L ook around, there are so many frowns, maybe we can turn those frowns upside down,
E mpty all of the ocean's trash, save the turtles, let's do it fast!
S o, think about how you can change the world and recycle!

Thomas McDonnell (11)

Koala Bears

K oalas are an endangered species
O ur natural habitat is forests and woodlands
A ustralia is our home
L ife is hard because of bushfires
A koala bear is a marsupial.

B ears have unique fingerprints
E ucalyptus leaves are my favourite food
A ction is needed to protect our environment
R espect us and look out for us, thank you!

Betsy Young (8)

Spring's Wonders

When the leaves rustle
When the bluebells sway
When you walk through the forest on a sunny day,
You can hear the birds singing and the rivers
flowing
But what catches the air is a nice wind blowing.
As the ferns unfurl
And the meadows dance,
You run around and skip and prance
You can smell the sweet cherry blossoms growing
on a tree
So come to the forest and play with me.

Milena Blackburn (9)

The Now And The Then

The now and the then,
Even the then was free,
Cooperated with the Earth,
Ostriches got to run free, a good time was
certainly guaranteed,
Committees' meetings got to be held in a tree,
Maybe the now will get the key,
Many have not seen a birch tree,
If you lived in the now you would not scream for
ice cream,
Trees are dying!
Temperatures are changing!
Every life counts!
Earth is dying! Save Earth!

Amelia Reilly (10)

No Other Planet

The plants and animals need the world to be green.
So pick up some litter and make it clean!
If you show the world you care,
You can read and help and then you can share!
We do not know what the future brings,
But if we help it now we can hope for great things!
So make your voice be heard, say, "Can't you see,
There is no other planet for you and me?"

Millie Purcell (9)

The Little Brown Bird

The tree shakes
The bird whistles
The goldfinches perch
On the stems of thistles

From summer to spring
They all do sing
Melodies drifting on the breeze
And please

Don't forget the little brown bird who's louder than
the rest
From the brambles to their nest
They tweet and trill
Their song fast and shrill

Louder than most
Loud as can be
The little wren perched in the old gnarled tree.

Hope Whittaker (11)

Make It Cleaner

The planet was beautiful, colourful and bright,
But now it's full of dirty and disgusting sights.

People are not caring about stinky rubbish
everywhere,
Animals are losing their homes, it's really not fair!

We need to pick up the rubbish and make the
planet tidy and clean,
Pollution is bad for you and me. When it's tidied it
will turn back green.

Sophia Tuffaha (5)

Types Of Goblins

G oblins are mostly green, blue and yellow.

O range goblins are rare/super rare.

B lue goblins are common and so are green goblins.

L ight purple goblins are super rare.

I ndia is one of the countries goblins live in.

N orth America has a lot of goblins.

S ome goblins are common, rare, super rare, special and challenges!

Muhammed Khizar Khan (8)

The Pretty... Bad? Weather

Sunny weather:
Hot sun shines so bright,
Put on your swimsuits,
Let's go for a dive!

Rainy weather:
Drops fall like sprinkles,
Falling down from the grey clouds,
As they are crying.

Snowy weather:
Small, fluffy, white balls,
Kids build fantastic snowmen,
Let's have fun all day!

Thundery weather:
Raging bolts, shock! Shock!
Please don't get electrified,
But stay in your homes!

Sue'ad Nazrana (9)

Importance Of Bees In Our Life

Bees provide sweet honey,
Which makes us lose money.
If there were no bees to collect nectar
Who would be the projector for nectar?

If bees were no more,
Who would have it or...
...bake a new recipe with it?

They are pollinators who help our environment.
We think they are benevolent insects
And help our wildlife and keep it healthy too!

Habib Parvez (7)

Environment

Nature outside,
Nature here and nature there,
Nature is everywhere!
We see the sea,
But soon it will be filled with litter.
The animals won't survive,
So we are going to help them thrive.
Bumblebees, black and yellow,
They help us get honey,
The least we can do is not to give money
Or be funny,
It is to look after their species.

Violet Hall (8)

Help The Trees

I am a tree
Swaying to and fro
There is something you've got to know!
People chop my family down
That makes me crossly frown
We help in so many different ways!

I am an owl
I never growl
I am innocent
I didn't do anything wrong!
People chop my home
That's wrong!
No time for a song
Help the trees, please!

Sophia Nanouri (9)

Trees

I love trees so much,
Because they help us breathe.

I love trees so much,
Because they are ginormous!

I love trees so much,
Because the branches are like magical wands.

I love trees so much,
Because the cheerful colours in autumn make me happy.

I love trees so much,
Because they made this paper.

I love trees so much
Because they have strong roots.

Trees are the crown of nature!

Evie Kairo (5)

Environmental Poem

Why should the Earth be harmed
And make all animals alarmed?
Why should animals eat plastic?
What if you ate elastic?

You should recycle all food
Even though you're not in the mood
Because that's kind of rude
You could get sued

Waste on the floor
What for?
Please no more
You don't want war

Keep floors clean
Like you've never been
Floors clear
All through the year.

Eleanor-Marie Hammerton (9)

Climate Buzz

The climate can change with a clap of your hands,
Prevent it and save our lands.

Turn off the lights or reuse your plastic,
Anything is good to make the heat less drastic.

Use less water, it can help the world,
Like solar energy is helping it too.

Different things make up to a lot,
Help stop this climate change, give it a shot!

Louisa Gribben (10)

The Spring

I like running free
And when the birds sing merrily
And the foxes growl
And the squirrels climb up,
When the new leaves swing gently in the wind
And the butterflies flap their wings
And the worms are underground eating the dirt.
I like to jump and twirl
And when the sun shines bright through the leaves,
It looks like a disco to me.

Elowyn Blackburn (6)

Nature Is A Part Of Us

Nature is a part of us.
All we do is destroy it.
So that will annoy it.
From elephant to mouse.
All with no house.
Dens washed up by the rain.
That causes such pain.
Wildfires that global warming inspires.
Floods that are vast run so fast as they pass.
Plant by plant, all crushed to the size of an ant.
All these bad things make nature sad things.
Nature is a part of us.

Jasmine Jenkins (9)

Animals

As the wind passes, nights fall
People gather to play football
Trees being chopped, trunks left alone
People not caring, still eating cones
Litter in the ocean, being trashed
Turtles in the ocean, sadly being smashed
Aeroplanes in the sky, gas littering the world
Animals like octopuses hurt, especially curled
As I finish this poem I must say
So many animals in the ocean lay.

Zeke Tunbridge (9)

Everything Is Nature

Everything is nature
God gave us this feature
Birds fly in the sky
And mountains are so high
How?
Everything is nature
The taste of the sky and that flavour
Which is greater
Everything is nature
The thing God gave us
Trees which are swaying
And foxes which are straying
Everything is nature
The leaves crunching
And the wind hushing
Everything is nature
But God made us...

Hajra Latif (9)

A Litter Day

Litter, litter everywhere,
All on the floor and in the air,
Tins not in bins,
Cans lie next to trams,
Glass all across the grass,
Wrappers out at sea,
If you don't believe me,
Come and see.

Clean up your act,
Before it's too late.
They say an apple a day keeps the doctor away,
What if a litter pick a day keeps the mess at bay!
Wouldn't that make your day?

Oscar Butler-Addis (10)

The Trees Of Life

I wake up one morning and look out,
I see a tree living free,
Sprouting with blossoms and containing a family
of possums,
Swaying back and forth, pointing north,
Giving life to the wild in style,
Feeding us oxygen, even if you're in Washington,
They are vital and have a title
So please, can we stop chopping the families of
trees?

Hibba Noor (11)

How Nature Works

Plant the trees, don't cut them down,
And pick your rubbish off the ground.

Please look after the planet well,
Respect all living things as well.
Fossil fuels are a no!
Electric cars are the way to go.

Please let this go worldwide,
So we can live a happy, good life,
And keep nature and animals alive.

Jack Dove (8)

Wildlife

W ildlife is amazing, living and colourful
I t's the most beautiful thing I've ever seen
L et it grow to save our Earth
D ark is when other creatures come out and play
L et our Earth do the work
I love our wildlife
F or the Earth
E arth is where our wildlife thrives.

Zara Firmin (9)

Save Our Precious World

I see the world being beautiful and magnificent!
I smell the air being fresh and clean.
I can touch the soft coat of the animals.
But I feel we are damaging our precious world and making our animals become extinct.
I would like to see us trying to recycle more and when we don't, *think!*
Is this going to hurt anything or ruin our atmosphere?

Harry Alessandar (12)

Orangutan, Orangutan

Orangutan, orangutan,
Race as fast as you can,
The rainforest is burning,
And the leaves are curling,
A giant forest fire,
That is drifting higher.

Orangutan, orangutan,
Threatened and endangered,
As you hear the birds crying,
Your playground is dying,
All because of palm oil,
You spoil...

William Thomas (10)

What Am I?

I am sometimes warm but often very cold
I am home to different species of fish
I am blue
I am very deep and powerful
I have lots of stones
I have volcanoes and sometimes lava flows into me
I am special
I am part of Planet Earth
Some people are throwing rubbish at me
Please don't litter in me.
What am I?

Answer: The ocean.

Rosie Dobson (6)

A Sad Tree

I am a tree, sad and alone
With all the trees cut and gone
Wild animals are losing homes
The danger of climate change should be known
I help my fellow beings
By filtering the air clean
To save Mother Earth
It's important to recycle to protect
Make our world fantastic
Please stop using plastic.

Bakhtawar Yousaf (6)

How To Make Our Planet Safe And Clean

To make our planet clean, we must plant more trees.

To make our planet clean, we must recycle so the seasons are proper.

To make our planet clean, we must stop sea pollution, so we can stop sea animals' extinction.

To make our planet clean, we must stop cutting down trees, so the birds have somewhere safe to stay and eat.

Joshua Tanimowo (6)

Stronger!

Litter everywhere,
Eco needs to be strong,
Let's be better for everyone's healthcare,
Debris is just so wrong,

We need to do something,
We need to do it now,
To make the world a better place,
We'll power through and never go down,

Litter everywhere,
What are we to do?
Let's make a stronger community,
To help me and you!

Isla Marshall (10)

The Pollution Cleaner

I'll be a pollution cleaner,
So the Earth can be more healthy.
I'll clean more than play,
And make a good day,
And I will be more wealthy!
I'll teach how to get rid of pollution,
So this can be our planet's solution!
I will be a recycler,
This will be Earth's conclusion!

Zuriel Oyedeji (7)

RPS - Recycling Population Story

Recycling is for the creativity of life
Pollution spoils the Earth with suffocation and dehydration.

The Earth does not have its own mind, so we are the rulers.
With recycling the Earth remains safe and healthy.

Wonderful results will come true and nature will remain sweetly.
We are responsible for our unique world so keep it!

Munachi Ojediran (8)

Litter

Litter, litter everywhere
No clean space
We seriously need to clean
It's bins we need to chase

All over the roads
The plastic lies
The animals will eat it
There's no surprise

We need to fix it
Fix all the sins of man
And we can do it
Hand in hand.

Zara Kelf (9)

Snakes

Either they are on the equator
Or shunned away for later
But really it's not what it seems
They are really beautiful creatures
Not bloodthirsty beasts
Their colours are so bright
May leave you a fright
But they are really just
A perfect plus
To this world.
Snakes!

Mahalakshmi Duraiarasan (11)

Nature Is Not Boring

Nature is green, so we are family
Roses are red, violets are blue
We throw rubbish so we should help too
Badgers eat worms, we use trees
So we are not family, we are bullies
We know what you are going through
But we are having a hard time too
If you wish I will try to make your wish come true.

Chrysanthea Davies Nkansa (7)

The Problem With Plastic

P ollution and plastic hurts our oceans
L andfills are getting too full
A nimals are getting hurt and their habitats
S ave our world from plastic
T he future will be better if we recycle
I can change the world
C hange your ways and recycle!

Isabella Henderson (8)

I Am A Tree

I am a tree with branches quite so long
Creatures like to live in me and sing their pretty songs
I love when koalas hug me, it makes me feel at home
When it rains I grow into the unknown
When I'm in the unknown I rustle and sway
But I never fall because my roots make sure I stay.

May Luna Estwick (6)

The Buzzy Bees!

The big yellow bees spread their pollen
And that's the way they help the trees
From flower to flower
And the dusty pollen, it falls from the bees
And lands on the trees.

My name is Buzz and we are the bees
And we can help save the world
But you must help too!

Ettie Jones (6)

Birds' Misery

Look at the birds in the sky,
And sadly watch them die.

Some are birds of prey,
Some feed on a plastic tray

Some birds are stuck in a cage,
Trapped, they grow in age.

Thirsty, hungry birds in the sun,
Fed on the offered water and bun.

For these creatures who are ill-fated,
I feel sad and devastated!

Divyansh Singh (10)

Lost Koalas

L ost koala,
O h no.
S uffering animals,
T rees turning black.

K oala babies calling for their mums,
O ut in the trees,
A ll alone.
L ittle lost koalas,
A lways loving.
S ave nature, wahoo!

Kat McCue (7)

The Grassy Planet

The Earth is where we live,
And we all need to give
Loads of work to keep it green.
So let's make sure to keep it clean
And also to keep it green.
You need to make it really clean
The sea is blue, the grass is green,
Make sure you put your rubbish in the bin!

Ajan Kola (7)

Our World

Our world is pretty
But soon it will be gritty
Forests are dropping
While we do our shopping
All over the world people feel fear
Children are shedding a tear
Our world is falling apart bit by bit
And people just don't get it
Our seas are full of plastic
But our world could be fantastic.

Beatrice Peacock (10)

Penguins And Polar Bears

Climate change makes the world hotter.
Ice melts and it is a bother.
Penguins and polar bears will lose their homes
Which is upsetting.
We need to look after our environment
And make the world better.
So that the penguins and polar bears can stay
together.

Sophia Mazouzi (6)

What Endangered Species Am I?

I weigh up to 180kg
I can stand up to 6 feet tall
I eat plants, ants and snails
I am scared of water
There are only 1,000 left of my kind in the wild
I live in a forest high up in the mountains.
What am I?

Answer: A mountain gorilla.

Brook Laycock (10)

Nature

N ature is getting harmed

A nd whoever does it is clearly not concerned

T he protestors are very alarmed about the planet

U nstoppable is the word for climate change

R age I bring from this

E veryone, stop climate change!

Ruby Fairweather (8)

No Planet B

As the Earth is left to die,
It is no good to cry.
As wildlife disappears,
We are left in fear.

The Earth gives way to flood and fire,
Man is left to hopeful desire,
As we are left to conspire
Disaster.

There is no Planet B!

Henry Bryers (10)

Help The Earth

I collect rubbish.
You collect rubbish.
Everyone collects rubbish.

I protect the trees.
You protect the trees.
Everyone protects the trees.

I save the animals.
You save the animals.
Everyone saves the animals.

I help the Earth.
You help the Earth.
Everyone helps the Earth.

Alexander Bak (7)

Never Let Nature Die

N ever let nature die,
A s we will regret it,
T o help nature is like helping a friend,
U nder the sea isn't where rubbish should be,
R ed pandas need to be kept safe,
E nd of the world should be stopped.

Isen Miller (9)

Sewage

S ad to see it in Exmouth sea

E xceedingly polluting our oceans

W ater unsafe for swimmers

A gainst sewage pollution surfers are

G etting into the waves on a rainy day

E nd the discharge, save our seas

Emily Oppersdorff (8)

Extinct

My favourite animal is an Emperor penguin,
It could be extinct if we do not protect the environment,
Some animals are already extinct like: Xerces blue butterfly, Crescent nail-tail wallaby, Schomburgk's deer,
Help the penguin,
No Planet B,
Save the world.

Frank Morris (10)

Violet

Where the roots hold,
Where all the oaks are old,
A purple beauty will rise,
Taking all the other dull things by surprise.
A shimmer, a glimmer, a glow,
What is this thing? I just don't know.
Is it a plum? A bluebell soon to come?
No, it's a violet.

Ava Rees (9)

I Love The World

I really want to save the world
I would never put rubbish on the ground
I only put rubbish in the bin

I love nature
I love when the lovely birds fly around in our garden
I love it when spring and beautiful flowers are here!

Sotirios Nanouris (5)

Let's Go Green!

G listening forests are getting destroyed
R ecycle your plastic waste
E ndangered species are nearly extinct
E arth is being suffocated by deforestation
N ow for the future let's plant more trees

Yuveer Goenka (9)

Recycle

Climate change is frightening,
We need to start recycling
Our plastic bottles,
Our paper bags and straws,
They fill our ocean floors.
So let's all make the change
To bring the Earth's temperature down again.

Willow Gage (6)

White Bunny

Carrot bunny
Free bunny
In danger bunny
Hopeless bunny
Rosy bunny
Honey bunny
Runny bunny
Crazy bunny
Fun bunny
Fluffy bunny
Funny bunny
Classy bunny
Wild bunny
Save the bunny.

Emilia Menezes-Shotter (7)

Save The Rainforest

The rainforest receives rain,
Just like the way we see the pain.
Tall trees, towering over with ease,
Powerful, precious plants.
Flowery, fast air flying through your hair.
Stop killing exotics, improvise and leave the
rainforest to thrive.

Isla Walker (11)

All About Nature

Nature is beautiful,
Nature is peaceful,
Nature is natural,
Nature is full of insects.

Nature is full of animals,
Nature is full of sea creatures,
Nature gives us clues,
Nature gives us love.

Alexandru Gabriel Paclisan (9)

Planet Earth

The world is great in a special way,
I see it is beautiful, please keep it this way,
Take your litter home
And look after our wildlife so no one can moan,
Let's all work together to protect our Planet Earth.

Layla Sullivan (6)

Pollution

I can see animals suffering,
Pollution is so bad I can basically taste it.
Can't you hear the cries of animals?
Why are we killing them?
They live here too,
Stop it! Stop it now!
And save our animals,
Save our home!

Lorelai Earl (11)

Magic Macaws

They squeak like mad,
Squabbling over food.
They look dazzling,
Like shiny, bright stars.
Silver, red, yellow, blue,
Feathers flying.
Dizzy, silly, funny,
Colourful in the canopy!

Alice Fletcher (5)

Litter

Litter is bad so please stop
I am recycling, you can too
Together we can save the animals
To help our planet, stop littering
Everybody, please help save our world
Recycle, recycle, recycle.

Phoebe Charlesworth (7)

All Because Of A Chocolate Bar

There are turtles and fish and sealife
Dying all because of a chocolate bar

They are made of plastic
If we bought food in cardboard boxes
Think about the animals you have saved.

Logan Watkin (9)

Nature

N ature is disappearing

A nd soon it will be gone

T urn to protect the planet

U se less paper

R ecycle more

E veryone can help to save Earth.

Priscilla Suresh (8)

Environment

B urning is bad for the environment
I slands will become trash
N ewts will become rubbish.

I t will not be fair
T urtles will get into rubbish.

Macy Ludgate (9)

Nature!

N ature surrounds us.

A dventure in the woods

T reasure God's creation.

U nder the stars

R ecycle with creativity.

E arth is our home.

Sophia Tang (8)

Nature In Three Different Colours

N atural

A nimal habitats,

T rees and bushes are shelter.

U nderstanding creatures live near the

R oots and feel the

E nchantment.

Kimberley Nindi (9)

Trees

Trees are green and tall, animals live in them.
They breathe carbon dioxide.
Trees are very important for our planet and life on Earth.
Trees give us oxygen so we can breathe.

Arthur Woods-Carrick (7)

The Ocean

O ur ocean needs help,
C reatures are dying,
E at with no plastic or wrappers,
A lways put litter in bins,
N ever litter in the sea.

Isla Reeves (7)

What You Can Do

I live on Planet Earth.
Earth is beautiful but it is messy.
Here is what you can do:
Pick up rubbish,
Plant trees and recycle.

I love Earth.

Jake Brzezinski (5)

Keeping Clean On Our Earth

I went to the playground
Because I wanted to play.
I saw three bits of litter.
I was sad.
We can pick up litter.
Make our Earth better.

Sion Guan (6)

Litter

A kennings poem

Ocean upsetter,
Sea destroyer,
Fish catcher,
Repulsive generator,
Bacteria attractor,
Earth absorber,
Humanity destroyer!

Sujay Thiruvallar (7)

Pollution

Petrol and diesel.
Worse than the measles.
Polluting our planet
Until it is famished
And has nothing left
Because of that pest.
Pollution.

Beatrice Isaac (9)

The Brilliant, Wonderful Trees

A kennings poem

An animal shelter,
A wood provider,
An oxygen supplier,
A forest ruler,
A fruit maker.

Sky Tsz Kwok (8)

YOUNG WRITERS INFORMATION

We hope you have enjoyed reading this book – and that you will continue to in the coming years.

If you're the parent or family member of an enthusiastic poet or story writer, do visit our website **www.youngwriters.co.uk/subscribe** and sign up to receive news, competitions, writing challenges and tips, activities and much, much more! There's lots to keep budding writers motivated!

If you would like to order further copies of this book, or any of our other titles, then please give us a call or order via your online account.

Young Writers
Remus House
Coltsfoot Drive
Peterborough
PE2 9BF
(01733) 890066
info@youngwriters.co.uk

Join in the conversation!
Tips, news, giveaways and much more!

 YoungWritersUK  YoungWritersCW  youngwriterscw

Scan me to watch The Big Green video!